Skills Builders

Spelling and Vocabulary

YEAR 4

Brenda Stones

RISING ★ STARS

Rising Stars UK Ltd, 7 Hatchers Mews, Bermondsey Street, London SE1 3GS
www.risingstars-uk.com

Every effort has been made to trace copyright holders and obtain their permission for the use of copyright materials. The publishers will gladly receive information enabling them to rectify any error or omission in subsequent editions.

All facts are correct at time of going to press.

Published 2013
Text, design and layout © 2013 Rising Stars UK Ltd

Project manager and editorial: Dawn Booth
Proofreader: Claire Shewbridge
Design: Words & Pictures Ltd, London
Cover design: Amina Dudhia
Acknowledgements: p.7 iStock/mightyisland; p.10 iStock/Deborah Connors; pp.14, 15, 21, 28, Dave Thompson; p.15 iStock/Larry Rains; p.36 i/Stock/Genestro; p.46 *Collins Junior Illustrated Thesaurus* with the permission of HarperCollins Publishers Ltd. © HarperCollins Publishers 2005, 2010. Collins ® is a registered trademark of HarperCollins Publishers Ltd.

British Library Cataloguing-in-Publication Data
A CIP record for this book is available from the British Library.

ISBN: 978-0-85769-700-4
Printed in Singapore by Craft Print International

Skills Builders: Spelling and Vocabulary

YEAR
4

Contents

How to use this book

The content and sequence of this series of Skills Builders on Spelling and Vocabulary are closely based on the revised National Curriculum for English.

Provided within this book are:

1 Active teaching of individual spelling rules.

2 Emphasis on regular patterns in English spelling.

3 Writing grids to reinforce these spelling patterns.

4 Spelling jars and pots in which children make collections of common spellings.

5 Thematic vocabulary pages.

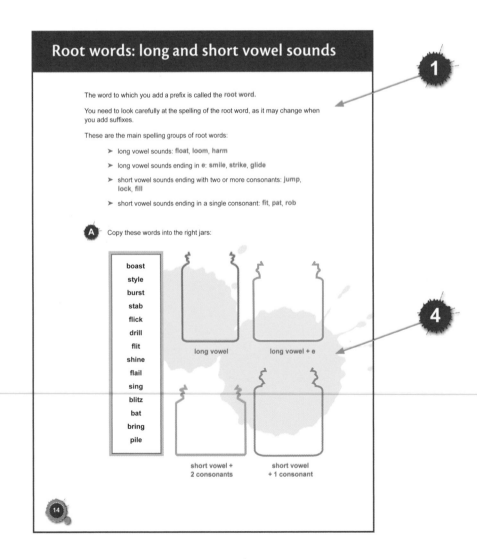

How to use this book

6   Occasional testing through dictation and word lists.

7   Three practical exercises that progress in difficulty.

8   Variety of layout, to help prepare for the new tests.

9   Encouragement of individual research in dictionaries and online.

10   Some more imaginative exercises on rhyme and alphabets.

11   'How did I do?' checks, for self-evaluation.

12   Answers are provided in a pull-out section for self-checking.

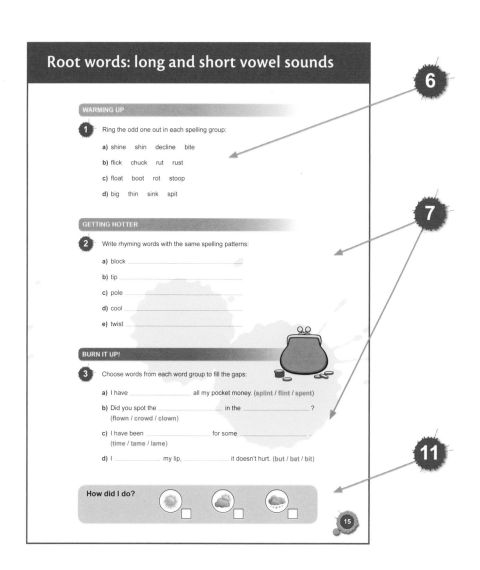

What do you need spelling for?

Why does spelling matter?

Do you think that spelling is important these days?

Or do you think that Spellcheck and texting mean you don't need to know how to get it right?

Actually people do judge you by your spelling, at every age in life.

Write down reasons why spelling might matter:

At school: ....

....

Taking exams: ....

....

Going to college: ....

....

Leaving messages for people: ....

....

Sending personal notes and greetings: ....

....

Applying for a job: ....

....

Doing a job with other people: ....

....

Why does spelling matter?

So how can you make your spelling better?

Write notes for these headings:

Making lists of words:

Using a dictionary:

Online word search:

Making corrections:

Testing yourself:

Practise dictation:

In your reading:

You may think that word classes are part of grammar.

But they are also part of spelling, because you change the spelling when you change the word class.

A reminder:

> ➤ **nouns** are naming words, and can be concrete, abstract or proper, e.g. dog, feeling, Paris

> ➤ **verbs** are doing words, and change by tense, e.g. dance, dancing, danced

> ➤ **adjectives** are describing words, and have comparative forms, e.g. big, **bigger**, **biggest**

> ➤ **adverbs** describe verbs, in terms of how, when or where, e.g. quickly, soon, there

A Turn these verbs into nouns:

i) invent _invention_   ii) inject _____

iii) act _____   iv) express _____

v) discuss _____   vi) confess _____

vii) extend _____   viii) expand _____

ix) comprehend _____

B Turn these nouns into adjectives:

i) poison _poisonous_   ii) danger _____

iii) mountain _____   iv) fame _____

v) nerve _____   vi) pore _____

vii) vary _____   viii) envy _____

ix) glory _____

C Turn these adjectives into adverbs:

i) quick _quickly_   ii) abrupt _____

iii) swift _____   iv) gentle _____

v) simple _____   vi) humble _____

vii) happy _____   viii) angry _____

ix) pretty _____

Revise: word classes

1 Match these words to their word class:

glamour
humorous
perform
confusion
musician
gentle
humbly
basic

noun
verb
adjective
adverb

2 Ring "odd one out" words in each word class, and say what class the rest of them are:

a) nerve   fame   state   precise _____

b) practise   do   previous   promise _____

c) famous   quickly   red   necessary _____

d) nation   curious   fashion   commotion _____

3 Turn each word from noun to adjective to adverb:

a) music   *musical* _____   *musically* _____

b) envy _____   _____

c) danger _____   _____

d) care _____   _____

e) hope _____   _____

f) anger _____   _____

How did I do?   ☐   ☐   ☐

9

Prefixes

Remember that a **prefix** goes **before** a word, and adds to its meaning.

 A Can you collect more sample words for this grid?

Prefix	Meaning	Sample words
ante-	before	anteroom
anti-	against	anti-slavery
inter-	between	Internet
mis-	wrongly	mistake
sub-	under	submarine
super-	over	supersize

 B Write the meaning of these words with prefixes:

i) antenatal _____

ii) anti-aircraft _____

iii) international _____

iv) misplace _____

v) subzero _____

vi) superhuman _____

Prefixes

 1 Choose the right words for the gaps:

subdivide   antidote   misspell   superior   supermarket

a) I often _____ words when I'm writing.

b) That _____ is the biggest around here.

c) Your _____ should stop my headache.

d) Let's _____ the apple into smaller pieces.

e) The best one is _____ to all the others.

 2 Write meanings for these words:

a) ante + bellum (= war) = _____

b) ante + diluvian (= flood) = _____

c) ante + meridian (= noon) = _____

d) inter + vene (= come) = _____

e) super + sede (= to sit) = _____

f) super + vise (= to look) = _____

3 Write your own sentences including these words:

a) interview _____

b) superstar _____

c) anti-clockwise _____

d) subheading _____

e) antiseptic _____

f) interact _____

How did I do? ☐   ☐   ☐

More prefixes

The following prefixes also have Latin or Greek origins.

 A Can you add more sample words?

Prefix	Meaning	Sample words
aero-	air	aeroplane
auto-	self	autograph
aqua-	water	aquarium
trans-	across	transport
ped-	foot	pedal
post-	after	postwar

B Write the meaning of these words with prefixes:

i)   aerospace ....

ii) autobiography ....

iii) aquaplane ....

iv) transatlantic ....

v)   pedestrian ....

vi) post-traumatic ....

More prefixes

1 Write meanings for these words:

    a) trans + late (= carry) = ⎯⎯⎯⎯⎯⎯⎯⎯⎯⎯⎯⎯⎯⎯⎯⎯

    b) pedo + meter (= measure) = ⎯⎯⎯⎯⎯⎯⎯⎯⎯⎯⎯⎯⎯

    c) post + meridian (= noon) = ⎯⎯⎯⎯⎯⎯⎯⎯⎯⎯⎯⎯⎯

    d) auto + didact (= teach) = ⎯⎯⎯⎯⎯⎯⎯⎯⎯⎯⎯⎯⎯

    e) post + script (= to write) = ⎯⎯⎯⎯⎯⎯⎯⎯⎯⎯⎯⎯⎯

    f) aqua + marine (= sea) = ⎯⎯⎯⎯⎯⎯⎯⎯⎯⎯⎯⎯⎯

GETTING HOTTER

2 What is the word for?

    a) across continents ⎯⎯⎯⎯⎯⎯⎯⎯⎯⎯⎯⎯⎯

    b) across the Alps ⎯⎯⎯⎯⎯⎯⎯⎯⎯⎯⎯⎯⎯

    c) works by itself ⎯⎯⎯⎯⎯⎯⎯⎯⎯⎯⎯⎯⎯

    d) pilots itself ⎯⎯⎯⎯⎯⎯⎯⎯⎯⎯⎯⎯⎯

    e) after death ⎯⎯⎯⎯⎯⎯⎯⎯⎯⎯⎯⎯⎯

BURN IT UP!

3 Write your own sentences including these words:

    a) transfer ⎯⎯⎯⎯⎯⎯⎯⎯⎯⎯⎯⎯⎯

    b) transit ⎯⎯⎯⎯⎯⎯⎯⎯⎯⎯⎯⎯⎯

    c) post-mortem ⎯⎯⎯⎯⎯⎯⎯⎯⎯⎯⎯⎯⎯

    d) autocue ⎯⎯⎯⎯⎯⎯⎯⎯⎯⎯⎯⎯⎯

    e) aerodynamic ⎯⎯⎯⎯⎯⎯⎯⎯⎯⎯⎯⎯⎯

How did I do?

 ☐ ☐ ☐

Root words: long and short vowel sounds

The word to which you add a prefix is called the **root word**.

You need to look carefully at the spelling of the root word, as it may change when you add suffixes.

These are the main spelling groups of root words:

➤ long vowel sounds: **float, loom, harm**

➤ long vowel sounds ending in **e**: **smile, strike, glide**

➤ short vowel sounds ending with two or more consonants: **jump, lock, fill**

➤ short vowel sounds ending in a single consonant: **fit, pat, rob**

 Copy these words into the right jars:

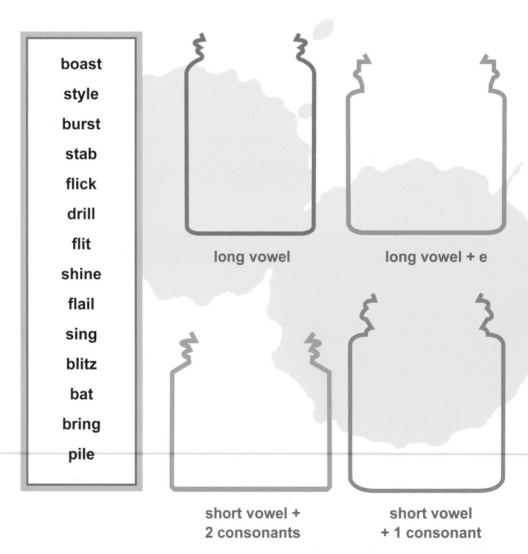

boast
style
burst
stab
flick
drill
flit
shine
flail
sing
blitz
bat
bring
pile

long vowel

long vowel + e

short vowel +
2 consonants

short vowel
+ 1 consonant

Root words: long and short vowel sounds

 1 Ring the odd one out in each spelling group:

    a) shine   shin   decline   bite

    b) flick   chuck   rut   rust

    c) float   boot   rot   stoop

    d) big   thin   sink   spit

GETTING HOTTER

 2 Write rhyming words with the same spelling patterns:

    a) block ....

    b) tip ....

    c) pole ....

    d) cool ....

    e) twist ....

BURN IT UP!

3 Choose words from each word group to fill the gaps:

    a) I have .... all my pocket money. (**splint / flint / spent**)

    b) Did you spot the .... in the .... ?
    (**flown / crowd / clown**)

    c) I have been .... for some ....
    (**time / tame / lame**)

    d) I .... my lip, ... it doesn't hurt. (**but / bat / bit**)

How did I do?

 ☐   ☐   ☐

Root words: word families

Do you remember what **word family** means?

It is a group of words built from the same root word, e.g. **family**, **familiar**, **unfamiliar**.

They may be built up from prefixes and suffixes, e.g. **rest**, **restful**, **unrestful**.

Or from different word classes, e.g. **teach** (**verb**), **teacher** (**noun**), **teaching** (**adjective**).

Word families help you to work out the spelling of a word, by going back to the root word.

Write the meanings of the different examples of word families below.

A Changing the prefix:

> **i)** transfer ....
>
> **ii)** refer ....
>
> **iii)** confer ....
>
> **iv)** defer ....

B Adding different suffixes:

> **i)** care + ful ....
>
> **ii)** care + less ....
>
> **iii)** care + less + ness ....
>
> **iv)** care + ful + ly ....

C Changing the word class:

> **i)** sail ....
>
> **ii)** sailor ....
>
> **iii)** sailing ....
>
> **iv)** sailed ....

Root words: word families

1 Add more words to each root word to make word families:

a) dance _____ *dancer   dancing* _____

b) progress _____

c) hope _____

d) sound _____

2 Build real words from these blocks:

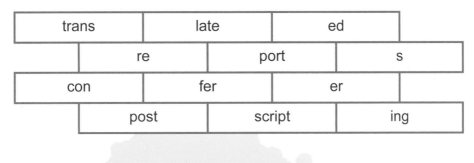

trans	late	ed

re	port	s

con	fer	er

post	script	ing

Remember the spelling rules for adding suffixes and for making verbs.

3 Choose the right words to fill the gaps:

a) At the end, I wrote a _____ . (**conscript / postscript / transcript**)

b) I am _____ to finish my homework. (**fail / failure / failing**)

c) Its shape is _____ than its box. (**rounding / rounded / rounder**)

d) This ice cream is my _____ . (**favour / favourite / favouring**)

e) Dinosaurs are _____ animals. (**prehistoric / historical / history**)

How did I do?

17

Vocabulary: word origins

Many English words have spellings and sounds that come from other languages.

 A   Can you add more examples?

Latin prefixes:
pre, post,
trans, inter

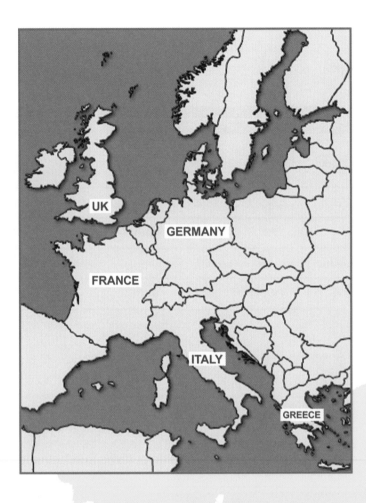

UK

GERMANY

FRANCE

ITALY

GREECE

Greek prefixes:
tele, auto,
psycho

Italian:
pizza, pasta

French suffix eau:
tableau, chateau, beauty

Greek y:
gym, myth, mystery

Vocabulary: word origins

 1   Match these words to their country of origin:

telephone
phonics
transport
beautiful
transcribe
postscript

Greece
France
Italy

GETTING HOTTER

2   We use a lot of food and drink words in European languages.

Do you know where these are from?

a) spaghetti _____

b) risotto _____

c) bolognese _____

d) moussaka _____

e) champagne _____

BURN IT UP!

3   Look up the meaning of these foreign words and phrases we use in English:

a) mea culpa _____

b) premier _____

c) tête-à-tête _____

d) id est _____

e) sic _____

How did I do?

Vowel digraph ou

How many sounds can this pair of vowels give us?

Spelling	Sound	Sample words
ou	ow	sound, lounge, pounce
ou	u	young, country, cousin
ou	oo	wound, rouble, mousse
our	or	course, source

The first sound, **ow**, is probably the most common.
The third sound is more common for words of foreign origin.

But there are several common words that follow the second sound; so when you hear 'u' in dictation, you have to think whether it might be one of the words spelt 'ou'.

A Fill in these words where '**u**' is spelt '**ou**':

> **i)** times two: d_____
>
> **ii)** a pair: c_____
>
> **iii)** difficulty: tr_____

B Now write the **-ing** form of each of the words in A:

> **i)** _____
>
> **ii)** _____
>
> **iii)** _____

C And the **-ed** form of each:

> **i)** _____
>
> **ii)** _____
>
> **iii)** _____

Vowel digraph ou

1 Copy these words into the right pots:

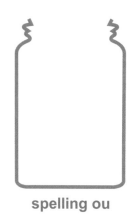

| stubble |
| trouble |
| couple |
| muddle |
| double |
| bubble |

spelling ou   spelling u

2 Write the right words in the blanks:

a) _____ people are called the _____ of today. (**youth / young**)

b) My _____ is Perthshire but my _____ is Scotland. (**country / county**)

c) If I _____ my money, I'll have a _____ of pounds. (**couple / double**)

d) It's _____ that I'm only _____ through. (**muddling / troubling**)

e) I have _____ of _____ in two places. (**cousins / couples**)

3 Follow the clues to write words in the white and yellow boxes that have the u sound spelled **ou**. The yellow column will tell you who's coming to stay.

A pair										
Not old										
Times two										
Least old										
Worrying										
My nation										

How did I do?

Vowel digraph ei, ey

This time we're looking at one sound, different spellings.

If you hear the sound **ay**, how many ways can it be spelled?

Sound	Spelling	Sample words
ay	ai	brain, plain
ay	ay	day, play
ay	a-e	fate, plate
ay	ei	vein, weigh, veil, feint, sleigh
ay	ey	they, obey, prey

The first three spellings are the most common, and you will have learned them earlier in your phonics lessons.

But the last two spellings are left to us from Old English spellings.

 A What are these words spelt **ei**?

> **i)** the number after seven ....
>
> **ii)** person next door ....
>
> **iii)** how heavy you are ....

 B Try these definitions:

> **i)** What is a bird of prey? ....
>
> **ii)** Where do you wear a veil? ....
>
> **iii)** What are feint lines? ....

Answers

Skills Builders

Spelling and Vocabulary

YEAR
4

Brenda Stones

Revise: word classes (pages 8–9)

A ii) injection iii) action iv) expression v) discussion vi) confession vii) extension viii) expansion ix) comprehension

B ii) dangerous iii) mountainous iv) famous v) nervous vi) porous vii) various viii) envious ix) glorious

C ii) abruptly iii) swiftly iv) gently v) simply vi) humbly vii) happily viii) angrily ix) prettily

1 *nouns:* glamour, confusion, musician
verbs: perform
adjectives: humorous, gentle, basic
adverb: humbly

2 a) precise, nouns b) previous, verbs c) quickly, adjectives
d) curious, nouns

3 b) envious, enviously c) dangerous, dangerously d) careful, carefully
e) hopeful, hopefully f) angry, angrily

Prefixes (pages 10–11)

A Answers will vary
antechamber, antecedent; antibacterial, antisocial; intermediate, interchange; misguide, misinterpreted; subset, subscript; superhero, superstore

B i) antenatal: before birth ii) anti-aircraft: against aircraft
iii) international: between nations iv) misplace: put in the wrong place
v) subzero: below zero vi) superhuman: more than human

1 a) misspell b) supermarket c) antidote d) subdivide e) superior

2 a) before the war b) before the flood (before Noah)
c) before noon (morning) d) come between
e) sit over (replace) f) look over

3 Answers will vary
a) I had an interview for the position.
b) He is my favourite superstar.
c) Take turns to answer anti-clockwise.
d) This text goes under a subheading.
e) Mum put some antiseptic on my cut.
f) You can interact with the game online.

More prefixes (pages 12–13)

A Answers will vary
aeronaut, aerosol; automatic, autocratic; aquarobics, aquamarine; transfer, transpose; pedestrian, pedicure; postglacial, postscipt

B i) space in the air ii) writing your own life story
iii) a plane that goes on water iv) across the Atlantic
v) someone on foot vi) after a trauma

1 a) carry across (between languages) b) measure footsteps c) afternoon
d) self-taught e) written after f) the colour of seawater (blue-green)

2 a) transcontinental b) transalpine c) automatic d) autopilot
e) post-mortem

3 Answers will vary
a) I will transfer the marbles into my other pocket.
b) My dad is in transit between Hong Kong and Dubai.
c) They will hold a post-mortem on his body.
d) Read the text from the autocue.
e) My paper plane is very aerodynamic.

Root words: long and short vowel sounds (pages 14–15)

A *long vowel:* boast, burst, flail
long vowel + e: style, shine, pile
short vowel + 2 consonants: flick, drill, bring, sing, blitz
short vowel + 1 consonant: flit, bat, stab

1 a) shin b) rut c) rot d) sink

2 Answers will vary
a) clock, stock b) lip, sip c) hole, whole d) fool, stool e) mist, whist

3 a) spent b) clown, crowd c) lame, time d) bit, but

Root words: word families (pages 16–17)

A Answers will vary
i) carry across ii) mention iii) discuss iv) put off

B Answers will vary
i) full of care (adj.) ii) without care (adj.) iii) without care (noun)
iv) with care (adverb)

C i) sail (noun) ii) person who sails (noun) iii) doing sailing (verb)
iii) did sailing (verb past tense)

1 Answers will vary
b) progression, progressing, progressed
c) hopeful, hopeless, hopefulness, hopelessness
d) soundless, sounding, sounded, resound

2 translate, translated, translates, translating; transfer, transferred, transfers, transferring; transport, transported, transports, transporter, transporting; transcript, transcripts; relate, related, relates, relating; refer, referred, refers, referring; report, reported, reports, reporter, reporting; confer, conferred, confers, conferring; conscript, conscripted, conscripts, conscripting; postscript, postscripts

3 a) postscript b) failing c) rounder d) favourite e) prehistoric

Vocabulary: word origins (pages 18–19)

A Answers will vary
Greek prefixes: bio, bi, geo, hyper, micro, mono, neo, pan, thermo, therm
Greek y: mysterious, gymnasium, gymnastic, mythology, cyst
Latin prefixes: ambi, circum, cis, juxta, per, pro, supra, subter
French suffix: gateau, bureau
Italian: balustrade, stanza, al fresco, artichoke, broccoli, diva

1 *Greece:* telephone, phonics;
France: beautiful;
Italy: transport, transcribe, postscript

2 a) Italy b) Italy c) Italy d) Greece e) France

3 a) my fault b) first c) head to head d) that is e) thus or so

Vowel digraph ou (pages 20–21)

A i) double ii) couple iii) trouble

B i) doubling ii) coupling iii) troubling

C i) doubled iii) coupled iii) troubled

1 *spelling ou:* trouble, couple, double;
  spelling u: stubble, muddle, bubble

2 **a)** Young, youth **b)** county, country **c)** double, couple
  d) troubling, muddling **e)** couples, cousins

3 couple, young, double, youngest, troubling, country,
  Answer: cousin

Vowel digraph ei, ey (pages 22–23)

A i) eight ii) neighbour iii) weight

B Answers will vary
  i) one that catches its food ii) on your head iii) very pale lines

1 weighs, weighing, weighed, weight, weighty, weightily; obeys, obeying,
  obeyed, obedience, obedient, obediently

2 **a)** vale, veil **b)** vein, vain **c)** weigh, way **d)** ate, eight **e)** faint, feint
  f) wait, weight **g)** slay, sleigh

3 obey, vein, neighbour, weight, eight, they
  Answer: eighty

Suffix -ing, -ed (longer verbs) (pages 24–25)

A forgetting, forgot; beginning, began; preferring, preferred; disliking,
  disliked; inflating, inflated; suggesting, suggested; transporting, transported;
  envying, envied

1 omitting, omitted; permitting, permitted; benefiting, benefited; remitting,
  remitted; restricting, restricted; committing, committed

2 bullying, bullied; defy, defied; destroying, destroyed; garden, gardened;
  mistaking, mistook; manufacture, manufacturing; foreseeing, foresaw

3 **a)** proceeded, proceeding **b)** succeeding, succeed
  c) forgotten, forgetting **d)** collapsing, collapsed

Suffix -ious, -eous (adjectives (pages 26–27)

A avaricious, cautious, ambitious, glorious, studious

B outrageous, rampageous

1 envious, fractious, gracious, spacious, furious, factious

2 **a)** studious, spacious **b)** furious, envious **c)** previous, precious
  d) cautious, ambitious **e)** outrageous, courageous

3 Answers will vary
  a) ahead of your years **b)** sarcastic **c)** feeling sick
  d) like mother of pearl **e)** glassy

Suffix -cher, -ture, -sure (nouns) (pages 28–29)

A *-cher:* voucher, poacher, marcher
  -sure: closure, tonsure
  -ture: vulture, posture, suture

1 **a)** moisture **b)** voucher **c)** posture **d)** creature **e)** tonsure

2 **a)** please **b)** enclose **c)** stretch **d)** thatch **e)** depart **f)** create

3 **a)** enclosure, pasture **b)** leisure, culture, vulture **c)** picture, pitcher
  d) stature, posture

Suffix -tion, -sion, -cian (nouns) (pages 30–31)

A *-tion:* demotion, exception
  -sion: television, decision, comprehension, devision
  -ssion: confession, passion, discussion, omission
  -cian: technician, politician

1 discussion, omission, inflation, confession, permission, direction,
  demotion, remission, confusion

2 permit, comprehend, extend, inflate, inject, admit, transmit, invent

3 Answers will vary
  a) person who studies maths **b)** great eagerness
  c) someone who works with beauty products **d)** a cut
  e) a dividing wall **f)** being sent to do something

Comparative adjectives and adverbs (page 33)

1 **a)** more gorgeous, most gorgeous **b)** crazier, craziest
  c) more wistful, most wistful **d)** more frantic, most frantic

2 **a)** better, best **b)** worse, worst **c)** more quickly, most quickly
  d) harder, hardest **e)** farther, farthest

3 *adjectives:* I caught the earlier train. That's a much harder rock. I caught
  a quicker train. I caught a faster train.
  adverbs: She arrived earlier. He's working harder. We arrived sooner.

Vocabulary: synonyms (pages 34–35)

A Answers will vary
  chuckled, droned, exclaimed, faltered, giggled, howled, intoned,
  joked, kidded, laughed, mimicked, nodded, opined, pleaded, quashed,
  replied, spoke, teased, uttered, voiced, wailed, x – nothing, yelled,
  zapped

1 Answers will vary
  strolled, loped, strode

2 Answers will vary
  scoffed, gulped, swallowed

3 Answers will vary
  happy, gentle, beautiful, good

Apostrophes: revision (pages 36–37)

A *contraction:* That man's in a hurry. That woman's gone home. The girl's
  in the bathroom.
  possession: The men's shoes are green. The women's shoes are blue.
  The horse's hooves are polished. The horses' hooves are not polished.
  The girls' bathroom is upstairs. Make way for the children's bus.
  The children's bus is late.

1 **a)** mustn't **b)** shan't **c)** won't **d)** father's **e)** dog's **f)** plant's

2 **a)** my sisters' socks **b)** my plants' leaves **c)** the snail's trail
  d) James's hat **e)** the chair's legs **f)** our mother's works

3 Answers will vary
  a) She didn't want to do her brother's chores.
  b) They weren't ready to get into Dad's car.
  c) He didn't kick Amir's football.
  d) They aren't going to go to Sian's party.
  e) I'm not sharing this with my sister's friend.
  f) He isn't included in Samir's team.

Homophones (pages 38–39)

A **i)** verb, noun **ii)** adjective, verb **iii)** noun, adjective **iv)** noun, adjective **v)** noun, adjective **vi)** adjective, noun **vii)** verb, noun **viii)** verb, noun **ix)** verb, noun **x)** noun, adjective **xi)** verb, noun **xii)** verb, noun **xiii)** noun, adjective **xiv)** verb, noun **xv)** verb, noun **xvi)** noun, adjective **xvii)** adjective, noun **xviii)** noun, verb **xix)** adjective, verb **xx)** verb, noun **xxi)** adjective, verb **xxii)** noun, verb **xxiii)** noun, verb **xxiv)** noun, verb **xxv)** adjective, noun

1 **a)** shake **b)** sauce **c)** mail **d)** floor **e)** some **f)** stair **g)** license **h)** steak **i)** earn

2 **a)** bare **b)** wait, weight **c)** caught, court **d)** ceiling, sealing **e)** check, cheque **f)** waste, waist **g)** wore, war **g)** sees, seize **i)** led, lead **j)** allowed, aloud **k)** freeze, frieze **l)** teems, teams

3 Answers will vary
   a) You aren't my aunt! **b)** I guessed you were a guest at the house.
   c) Can you heal my heel? **d)** She knows about my nose.
   e) The maid made the bed. **f)** I have to write the right words.

Common errors: double letters (pages 40–41)

A **i)** illegal **ii)** coolly **iii)** immigrate **iv)** cooperate **v)** wholly **vi)** accelerate **vii)** unnerve **viii)** interrupt

1 **a)** preferred, preferring **b)** beginner, beginning **c)** omitted, omitting, omission **d)** peacefully **e)** tinny **f)** hopefully, hopelessly, hopelessness, hopefulness

2 **a)** hitchhiking **b)** fizzy **c)** runny **d)** sufficient **e)** possess **f)** immediately

3 Answers will vary
   accelerate, nodded, been, off, dogged, hitchhike, radii, hajj, bookkeeper, mulled, hammer, runny, book, appear, saqqi, hurry, ass, tatty, vacuum, spivvy, arrowwood, (no x), sayyid, fizz

Using a thesaurus (page 43)

1 alphabetical order: down the sides of the pages
   running head: in mauve at the top
   headword: main word in blue
   word class: in black caps after each headword
   definition: in black below the headword
   synonyms: in bold black under each headword
   sample sentence: in italics after each synonym

2 alphabetical order: find the right letter of the alphabet
   running head: find which words are on that page
   headword: find the main word you need
   word class: know the grammar of the word
   definition: understand what the word means
   synonyms: find alternative words
   sample sentence: read the new words used in context

3 **a)** The first is for things, the second for people.
   b) alphabetical order
   c) enchanting, gorgeous, incredible, magnificent, spectacular, lovely
   d) attractive, graceful, pretty, stunning

Testing: word list (page 44)

1 **a)** shinier **b)** mountainous **c)** comprehension **d)** monkeys' **e)** medicine **f)** disappear **g)** business **h)** synonym **i)** thesaurus **j)** piece **k)** electrician **l)** neighbour **m)** humbly **n)** trans **o)** conscience **p)** regularly **q)** medal **r)** treasure, pleasure, leisure **s)** strength **t)** island

Vowel digraph ei, ey

1 Write in all these parts for the two verbs:

	weigh	obey
-s		
-ing		
-ed		
noun		
adjective		
adverb		

2 Write the right words in the blanks:

a) A _____ is a valley; a _____ covers your head. (**veil / vale**)

b) A _____ carries blood; being proud is being _____ . (**vein / vain**)

c) How much do you _____ ? Do you know the _____ ? (**way / weigh**)

d) You _____ how much food? Is that _____ kilos? (**ate / eight**)

e) In the heat I might _____ . These lines are too _____ . (**faint / feint**)

f) Please will you _____ ? I'm just getting my _____ . (**wait / weight**)

g) To kill is to _____ . Father Christmas rides in a _____ . (**slay / sleigh**)

3 Answer the question using the white boxes for your letters and the yellow column will reveal a number!

Do what you're told												
Carries blood												
Person next door												
How heavy												
Number before nine												
Them												

How did I do?

Suffix -ing, -ed (longer verbs)

Now we come back to adding suffixes at the end of verbs.

What happens if the verb has more than one syllable?

The same spelling rules apply to the last syllable, following the word groups we made in "Root words: long and short vowel sounds", page 14:

➤ most words, just add **-ing** or **-ed**: **construct, constructing, constructed**

➤ long vowel sounds ending in **e**, take off the **e**: **relate, relating, related**

➤ short vowel sounds ending in one consonant, usually double the last letter: **prefer, preferring, preferred**

➤ words ending in **y** after a consonant: keep the **y** for **-ing**, change to **i** before **-ed**: **reply, replying, replied**

But we shall add two exceptions:

➤ if you stress the first syllable, you don't double the last letter: **limited, benefited**

➤ some words have an irregular past tense: **mistake, mistook**; **begin, began**

 A   Fill in the verb parts for these longer verbs:

Root verb	-ing	-ed or past tense
forget		
begin		
prefer		
dislike		
inflate		
suggest		
transport		
envy		

Suffix -ing, -ed (longer verbs)

WARMING UP

1 Complete these verb parts:

Root verb	-ing	-ed or past tense
omit		
permit		
benefit		
remit		
restrict		
commit		

GETTING HOTTER

2 Fill all the boxes in this grid:

Root verb	-ing	-ed or past tense
bully		
	defying	
destroy		
	gardening	
mistake		
		manufactured
foresee		

BURN IT UP!

3 Fill the gaps with the right parts of the verbs given:

a) (**proceed**) I have .... and I will be ....

b) (**succeed**) I am .... at this, as I always ....

c) (**forget**) I have .... , and am always ....

d) (**collapse**) I am .... with the strain, as you have ....

How did I do?

Suffix -ious, -eous (adjectives)

We have looked at turning nouns into adjectives by adding **-ous**:

> **danger, dangerous; fame, famous; nerve, nervous**

Adjectives can also have the suffix **-ious**, and these may come from nouns ending in **-ce**, **-ion**, **y**.

 A Fill in the **-ious** adjectives for these nouns.

The first one has been done for you.

	-ious
price	precious
avarice	
caution	
ambition	
glory	
study	

Others don't have a root noun:

> **serious, previous, obvious**

The suffix **-eous** comes from nouns ending in **-ge**.

 B Fill in the **-eous** adjectives for these nouns.

The first one has been done for you.

	-eous
courage	courageous
outrage	
rampage	

And also **gorgeous**, **nauseous**.

Suffix -ious, -eous (adjectives)

 1 Fill in **-ous** adjectives from these nouns:

	-ous
envy	
fraction	
grace	
space	
fury	
faction	

 2 Write the right words in these blanks:

a) When I study a lot I'm _____ ; in a space that's _____ .
(**spacious / studious**)

b) When I'm angry I feel _____ ; when I'm jealous I feel _____ .
(**envious / furious**)

c) The one before was _____ ; the one after is more _____ .
(**precious / previous**)

d) I'm wary, so I'm _____ , but I want to do well, so I'm _____ .
(**cautious / ambitious**)

e) He's wild, he's _____ , but he's steely, he's _____ .
(**courageous / outrageous**)

3 Look up the meanings of these words and write down what they mean.

a) precocious _____

b) facetious _____

c) nauseous _____

d) nacreous _____

e) vitreous _____

How did I do?
 ☐   ☐   ☐

27

Suffix -cher, -ture, -sure (nouns)

These three endings sound a bit similar, but they tend to have different roots.

Suffix	Origin	Sample words
-cher	comparative adjectives **-er** forms from verbs ending in **-ch**	richer catcher, butcher, thatcher, stretcher, pitcher, teacher
-ture	most common spelling for stand-alone words	picture, adventure, creature, furniture, departure, mixture, culture, feature, pasture, denture, moisture
-sure	sometimes from verbs ending in **-se**	pleasure, enclosure, measure, treasure, leisure

 A   Copy these words into the right jars:

voucher   vulture   posture

closure   tonsure

poacher   marcher   suture

-cher   -sure   -ture

Suffix -cher, -ture, -sure (nouns)

1 From the lists opposite, what is the word for:

a) wetness _____

b) discount _____

c) how you stand _____

d) an animal _____

e) a bald patch _____

2 What are the verbs from which these nouns are built?

a) pleasure _____

b) enclosure _____

c) stretcher _____

d) thatcher _____

e) departure _____

f) creature _____

3 Choose **-ure** words from this list to fill the gaps:

culture pasture posture pitcher leisure enclosure
stature picture vulture

a) A field is an _____ or a _____ .

b) I spend my _____ time being a _____ .

c) A still life may be a _____ of a _____ .

d) When I stand, my _____ gives me a good _____ .

How did I do?

Suffix -tion, -sion, -cian (nouns)

There are lots of nouns that end with the sound "**shun**". How do you spell them?

Here are just some of the answers. It can help to go back to the spelling of the root word.

Spelling	When	Examples
-tion	The most common spelling, including **-ation**, **-ition**, **-ction**. Use when the root word ends in **-t** or **-te**.	action injection
-sion	Use when the root word ends in **-d** or **-de**.	expansion extension
-ssion	Use when the root word ends in **-ss** or **-mit**.	expression permission
-cian	Use when the root word ends in **-c** or **-cs**; these are often words for jobs.	musician magician
-shion	These are just exceptions! They tend to come from foreign words.	cushion fashion

 A   Add these words to the right boxes of examples above:

- ➤ technician
- ➤ passion
- ➤ politician
- ➤ comprehension

- ➤ demotion
- ➤ television
- ➤ decision
- ➤ exception

- ➤ confession
- ➤ discussion
- ➤ omission
- ➤ division

Suffix -tion, -sion, -cian (nouns)

1 Try making these verbs into nouns with a suffix ending **-ion**.

Verb	Noun
complete	completion
discuss	
omit	
inflate	
confess	

Verb	Noun
permit	
direct	
demote	
remit	
confuse	

2 What are the root verbs from which these nouns are built?

	permission
	comprehension
	extension
	inflation

	injection
	admission
	transmission
	invention

3 What are the meanings of these words?

a) mathematician

b) passion

c) beautician

d) incision

e) partition

f) mission

How did I do?

 ☐   ☐   ☐

31

Comparative adjectives and adverbs

You have learned that you make comparative adjectives by adding **-er** and **-est**, following the spelling rules for changing the last letter:

	-er	-est
cool	cooler	coolest
wise	wiser	wisest
big	bigger	biggest
tiny	tinier	tiniest

What about longer adjectives? You don't say **beautifuller**; you say **more beautiful**.

The only longer adjectives that add **-er** and **-est** are ones ending in **y: angrier, shinier**.

But adverbs can be longer words: **beautifully, necessarily**.

To make the comparative form of adverbs, you usually use **more** and **most**:

> **She arrived more quickly** not **She arrived quicker**

because **quicker** is a comparative **adjective** not a comparative **adverb**.

The only adverbs that have comparative forms are:

Adverb	Comparative	Superlative
fast	faster	fastest
early	earlier	earliest
hard	harder	hardest
well	better	best
badly	worse	worst
far	farther	farthest
soon	sooner	soonest

Comparative adjectives and adverbs

 1 Write the comparative and superlative adjectives:

a) This is gorgeous; that is _____ ; those are the

_____ .

b) He is crazy; she is _____ ; they are the

_____ .

c) I am wistful; he is _____ ; she is the

_____ .

d) She is frantic; he is _____ ; we are the

_____ .

GETTING HOTTER

 2 Write the comparative and superlative adverbs:

a) She did well; he did _____ ; I did _____ .

b) We did badly; they did _____ ; you did _____ .

c) I left quickly; she left _____ ; he left _____ .

d) You worked hard; I worked _____ ; she worked _____ .

e) I ran far; you ran _____ ; they ran _____ .

BURN IT UP!

 3 Decide whether each comparative word is an adjective or adverb and draw a line to the correct word class.

I caught the earlier train.
She arrived earlier.
He's working harder.
That's a much harder rock.
I caught a quicker train.
I caught a faster train.
We arrived sooner.

adjective
adverb

How did I do?

Vocabulary: synonyms

Synonyms are words that mean the same thing.

You can look them up in a **thesaurus** (see "Using a thesaurus", page 42).

 Try writing synonyms for **said**, one for each letter of the alphabet!
The first two have been done for you.

a *argued*

b *bantered*

c

d

e

f

g

h

i

j

k

l

m

n

o

p

q

r

s

t

u

v

w

x

y

z

Vocabulary: synonyms

1 Now write synonyms for walked:

2 Try synonyms for ate:

3 Finally, write synonyms for nice:

How did I do?

35

Apostrophes: revision

Remember when you need an apostrophe:

➤ for missing letters or contractions: e.g. **she'll**, **we've**, **it's**

➤ for singular possession, e.g. the **lady's** shoes, the **boy's** helicopter, the **man's** ties

➤ for plural possession, e.g. the **ladies'** shoes, the **boys'** helicopter, the **men's** ties

You **never** use an apostrophe:

➤ for plurals, e.g. **TVs**, **tomatoes**, **707s**

➤ possessive pronouns, e.g. **hers**, **theirs**, **its**

 A Match each sentence to one of the uses.

The men's shoes are green.
That man's in a hurry.
The women's shoes are blue.
That woman's gone home.
The horse's hooves are polished.
The horses' hooves are not polished.
The girl's in the bathroom.
The girls' bathroom is upstairs.
Make way for the children's bus.
The children's bus is late.

contraction
possession

Apostrophes: revision

1 Write contractions for the underlined words:

a) She <u>must not</u> go. _____

b) We <u>shall not</u> hear. _____

c) They <u>will not</u> come. _____

d) Her <u>father is</u> on his way. _____

e) His <u>dog has</u> lost his bone. _____

f) Their <u>plant is</u> wilting. _____

2 Turn these into possessive phrases:

a) The socks of my sisters _____

b) The leaves of my plants _____

c) The trail of the snail _____

d) The hat of James _____

e) The legs of the chair _____

f) The works of our mother _____

3 Write sentences that include one word with an apostrophe for contraction and one word with an apostrophe for possession:

a) _____

b) _____

c) _____

d) _____

e) _____

f) _____

How did I do?

Homophones

Homophones are words that sound almost the same but are spelt differently and have different meanings.

 A All these homophones are different word classes. Write their word classes beside them, to help you remember why they are spelt differently.

i) aren't / aunt ....

ii) blue / blew ....

iii) board / bored ....

iv) bread / bred ....

v) currant /current ....

vi) dear / deer ....

vii) flee / flea ....

viii) guessed / guest ....

ix) heal / heel ....

x) horse / hoarse ....

xi) knows / nose ....

xii) lain / lane ....

xiii) loan / lone ....

xiv) made / maid ....

xv) missed / mist ....

xvi) moor / more ....

xvii) pale / pail ....

xviii) practice / practise ....

xix) raw / roar ....

xx) read / reed ....

xxi) right / write ....

xxii) road / rode ....

xxiii) seam / seem ....

xxiv) side / sighed ....

xxv) sole / soul ....

Homophones

WARMING UP

 1 Write homophones for these words:

a) sheikh _____ **b)** source _____ **c)** male _____

d) flaw _____ **e)** sum _____ **f)** stare _____

g) licence _____ **h)** stake _____ **i)** urn _____

GETTING HOTTER

 2 Fill these gaps with the right spellings:

a) Watch out for the hunter with a _____ behind! (**bare / bear**)

b) Can you _____ while I check my _____? (**weight / wait**)

c) I was _____ for speeding outside the _____. (**court / caught**)

d) Under the _____ I'm _____ a parcel. (**ceiling / sealing**)

e) I must _____ how much the _____ is for. (**check / cheque**)

f) What a _____ that your _____ is so small. (**waist / waste**)

g) The soldiers _____ uniform in the _____. (**wore / war**)

h) She _____ what she can _____. (**seize / sees**)

i) I'm _____ to believe that _____ gives you asthma. (**led / lead**)

j) I'm not _____ to sing _____. (**aloud / allowed**)

k) We'll _____ in the cold below the wall _____. (**freeze / frieze**)

l) The river _____ with fish, which is good for our fishing _____. (**teems / teams**)

BURN IT UP!

3 Choose six homophones from the opposite page and write sentences including both:

a) _____

b) _____

c) _____

d) _____

e) _____

f) _____

How did I do?

 ☐ ☐ ☐

Common errors: double letters

A key part of good spelling is knowing when to use double letters. So here are some basic rules:

1. There are two **vowels** that are often doubled to make long vowel sounds, **oo** and **ee**:

   > **boot, tool, feel, freeze**

2. After a **short vowel sound** ending with a single consonant, you double the last letter before adding a suffix:

   > **patter, sitting, muddle, cutting, clipper, betting, potter**

3. Some **suffixes** have double letters: **ness** and **less**, but not **ful**.

4. **Prefixes** that end with consonants can cause double consonants:

   > **surround, misshapen**

   and some prefixes change to create double letters:

   > **illegible, illegal, accede, acclaim**

5. Then there are words that have double consonants in the middle:

   > **appear, accident, accommodate, exaggerate, succeed, necessary**

   So it helps to break down words into their prefix, suffix and root word; and then just learn the difficult ones!

 A Do these word sums, which produce double letters:

i) il + legal = ...

ii) cool + ly = ...

iii) im + migrate = ...

iv) co + operate = ...

v) whole + ly = ...

vi) ac + celerate = ...

vii) un + nerve = ...

viii) inter + rupt = ...

Common errors: double letters

1 Write forms of these words that need double letters:

a) prefer

b) begin

c) omit

d) peaceful

e) tin

f) hope

2 These words all have double letters:

a) thumbing a lift

b) a drink with bubbles

c) liquid honey

d) enough

e) to own

f) right now

3 Can you write a word for each letter of the alphabet where it is doubled? They may not all be possible ... The first two have been done for you.

a _bazaar_

b _bubble_

c

d

e

f

g

h

i

j

k

l

m

n

o

p

q

r

s

t

u

v

w

x

y

z

How did I do?

41

Using a thesaurus

Here is a page from the *Collins Junior Thesaurus*:

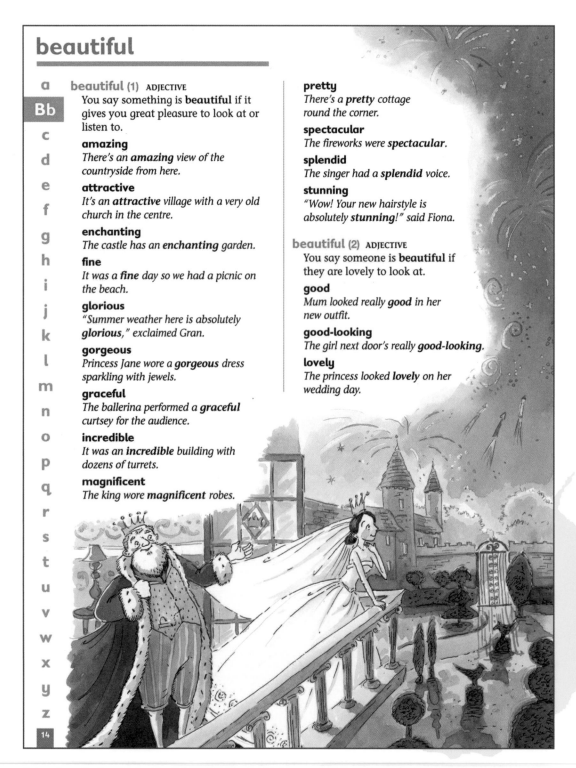

beautiful

a
Bb
c
d
e
f
g
h
i
j
k
l
m
n
o
p
q
r
s
t
u
v
w
x
y
z
14

beautiful (1) ADJECTIVE
You say something is **beautiful** if it gives you great pleasure to look at or listen to.

amazing
There's an **amazing** view of the countryside from here.

attractive
It's an **attractive** village with a very old church in the centre.

enchanting
The castle has an **enchanting** garden.

fine
It was a **fine** day so we had a picnic on the beach.

glorious
"Summer weather here is absolutely **glorious**," exclaimed Gran.

gorgeous
Princess Jane wore a **gorgeous** dress sparkling with jewels.

graceful
The ballerina performed a **graceful** curtsey for the audience.

incredible
It was an **incredible** building with dozens of turrets.

magnificent
The king wore **magnificent** robes.

pretty
There's a **pretty** cottage round the corner.

spectacular
The fireworks were **spectacular**.

splendid
The singer had a **splendid** voice.

stunning
"Wow! Your new hairstyle is absolutely **stunning**!" said Fiona.

beautiful (2) ADJECTIVE
You say someone is **beautiful** if they are lovely to look at.

good
Mum looked really **good** in her new outfit.

good-looking
The girl next door's really **good-looking**.

lovely
The princess looked **lovely** on her wedding day.

Taken from *Collins Junior Illustrated Thesaurus* with the permission of HarperCollins Publishers Ltd.
© HarperCollins Publishers 2005, 2010. Collins ® is a registered trademark of HarperCollins Publishers Ltd.

Using a thesaurus

WARMING UP

1 Find and match each feature from the thesaurus:

Feature	Where is it?
alphabetical order	in italics after each synonym
running head	in black below the headword
headword	main word in blue
word class	in bold black under each headword
definition	in mauve at the top
synonyms	in black caps after each headword
sample sentence	down the sides of the pages

GETTING HOTTER

2 What do these features help you do? Match the right answers.

Feature	It helps you
alphabetical order	find the main word you need
running head	read the new words used in context
headword	know the grammar of the word
word class	find which words are on that page
definition	find the right letter of the alphabet
synonyms	find alternative words
sample sentence	understand what the word means

BURN IT UP!

3 Answer the following questions:

a) What is the difference between **beautiful** definitions 1 and 2?

b) In what order are the synonyms given?

c) Which six synonyms could the picture be illustrating?

d) Which synonyms from the first meaning could also be used for the second meaning?

How did I do?

43

Testing: word list

This is a mixture of words from this book and words from the programme of study.

 1 Answer the following questions:

a) comparative form of shiny ⋯⋯⋯⋯⋯⋯⋯⋯⋯⋯

b) the adjective from mountain ⋯⋯⋯⋯⋯⋯⋯⋯⋯⋯

c) the noun from comprehend ⋯⋯⋯⋯⋯⋯⋯⋯⋯⋯

d) the possessive plural of monkey ⋯⋯⋯⋯⋯⋯⋯⋯⋯⋯

e) a drink that cures you ⋯⋯⋯⋯⋯⋯⋯⋯⋯⋯

f) the negative verb from appear ⋯⋯⋯⋯⋯⋯⋯⋯⋯⋯

g) the noun from busy ⋯⋯⋯⋯⋯⋯⋯⋯⋯⋯

h) a word that means the same ⋯⋯⋯⋯⋯⋯⋯⋯⋯⋯

i) a book for the above ⋯⋯⋯⋯⋯⋯⋯⋯⋯⋯

j) homophone of peace ⋯⋯⋯⋯⋯⋯⋯⋯⋯⋯

k) person who works with electrics ⋯⋯⋯⋯⋯⋯⋯⋯⋯⋯

l) the person next door ⋯⋯⋯⋯⋯⋯⋯⋯⋯⋯

m) the adverb from humble ⋯⋯⋯⋯⋯⋯⋯⋯⋯⋯

n) prefix meaning across ⋯⋯⋯⋯⋯⋯⋯⋯⋯⋯

o) con + science = ⋯⋯⋯⋯⋯⋯⋯⋯⋯⋯

p) the adverb from regular ⋯⋯⋯⋯⋯⋯⋯⋯⋯⋯

q) homophone of meddle ⋯⋯⋯⋯⋯⋯⋯⋯⋯⋯

r) rhymes with measure ⋯⋯⋯⋯⋯⋯⋯⋯⋯⋯

s) noun from strong ⋯⋯⋯⋯⋯⋯⋯⋯⋯⋯

t) land surrounded by water ⋯⋯⋯⋯⋯⋯⋯⋯⋯⋯

How did I do? ☐ ☐ ☐

44